Danny's Mum

Illustrated by Lesley Saddington

W,

6

Danny was sitting in his favourite spot in the garden.

He was thinking about lots of different things.

He began to think about his mum.

He wondered what she was doing.

Was she happy or was she sad?

Was she thinking about him?

prison

scho

8 Danny's house

prison

Danny's mum did not live with him because she had been sent to prison.

She was there with lots of other women and some of them were mums too.

When Danny was told his Mum had gone to prison he did not know what to do.

Sometimes Danny felt angry because his mum had gone away.
Sometimes he felt frightened, sometimes he felt sad, but most of all he missed her.
He thought he should be grown-up and not show he was unhappy.
Danny did not tell anyone how he felt.

At school, Danny's friend Paul asked him where his mum had gone.
Danny did not want to tell him.
He wanted it to be his secret.
When his teacher asked Danny where his mum was, he didn't tell her either.

The teacher asked whose parents were coming to sports day.
Paul said his dad couldn't come as he was in prison.
At playtime Danny told Paul all about his mum.
They told each other stories about when they visited prison.

One day Danny had a special visitor who knew his mum was in prison.

She played games with him and talked to him about his mum. Next time she came, she said, "Mummy still loves you, even though she's in prison."

This made Danny feel much better.

Danny went to visit his mum in prison.
It looked like a big castle.
He was so happy to see her.
She was just the same as she had always been.
She told him about her life in prison.
Danny was very sad saying goodbye, but he knew he would see
her again soon.

Danny now talks about his mum.
He's glad he is not the only person with a mum or dad in
prison.
Sometimes Danny and Paul play together and share their news.

Need help?

Prisoners' families helpline

Call us free on
0808 808 2003

The Prisoners' Families Helpline is the national helpline supporting the friends and families of prisoners. They can give practical information about visiting and keeping in touch, how the prison system works and many more issues. They can also talk through how imprisonment can affect children and how to support children who have a parent in prison.

www.prisonersfamilieshelpline.org.uk